Circle true or false.

1. Catholics use symbols and rituals in liturgy. T F
2. People did not use symbols until recent times. T F
3. Expressing beliefs symbolically is part of being human. T F
4. Most rituals are complicated. T F
5. A characteristic of ritual is that it is interpersonal. T F

Circle the letter beside the best answer.

6. The public prayer of the Church is called
   a. symbol.
   b. ritual.
   c. liturgy.
   d. sign.

7. Native Americans saw no need to build sacred spaces because they
   a. did not think symbolically.
   b. did not believe in any kind of god.
   c. moved around too much.
   d. believed all the land was sacred.

8. Signs and symbols put us in touch with
   a. Native Americans.
   b. geography.
   c. things we cannot see.
   d. surface realities.

9. For the Greeks, ___ was the dwelling place of the gods.
   a. Machu Picchu
   b. Mount Olympus
   c. Medicine Mountain
   d. the mosque

10. Which of the following is *not* a characteristic of ritual? Ritual is
   a. interpersonal.
   b. permanent.
   c. repetitive.
   d. acted out.

11. Which of the following is *not* truly a "sacred place."
   a. Christian churches
   b. Muslim mosques
   c. the Temple wall in Jerusalem
   d. the Mississippi River

12. All ___ involve ritual.
   a. Church writings
   b. experiences
   c. the sacraments
   d. symbols

13. Circle the *false* statement. Rituals
   a. are symbolic actions.
   b. have been part of the human experience from earliest times.
   c. are mysterious and unknowable.
   d. meet deep human needs.

14. Rituals
   a. are more significant when done alone.
   b. are not used in weddings.
   c. are boring if repeated.
   d. help us make sense of life's mysteries.

15. For Catholics all our churches
   a. are mysterious.
   b. are sacred spaces.
   c. are like Shinto shrines.
   d. are "cities of the dead."

D1418466

1

Fill in the blank with the correct word(s).

16. The sacred places, objects, and actions of the _____
_____ relate to the belief that Jesus Christ became one of us.

17. Many cultures and religions built their sacred places on
_____ to try to be closer to their gods.

18. _____ are symbols connected in meaningful action.

19. The _____ son was greeted by his father with love
and forgiveness.

20. A _____ is something that stands for something else.

For Extra Credit

Think of some symbols found and some rituals performed in your home. How
do they enrich your family life?

Circle true or false.

1. When Catholics pray together, we celebrate in and through symbolic activity. T F

2. Rituals meet deep human needs. T F

3. Liturgy is a work by and for the priests of the Church only. T F

4. Liturgical prayer is always prayer to the Blessed Trinity. T F

5. Liturgy is both communal and personal. T F

Circle the letter beside the best answer.

6. An object or action that stands for something else is
   a. a visual aid.
   b. one of the five senses.
   c. a ritual.
   d. a symbol.

7. Circle the *false* statement.
   a. Only the Eucharist uses symbol and ritual.
   b. An understanding of ritual is essential for a mature understanding of Catholic worship.
   c. Ritual draws us deeply into the faith it expresses.
   d. Ritual uses symbolic movements.

8. Which of the following is *not* a symbol in Catholic worship?
   a. sitting and standing
   b. turning towards the east
   c. singing together
   d. incense

9. Actions repeated in formal and set ways are
   a. rituals.
   b. symbols.
   c. always public.
   d. never prayerful.

10. In the Church the word *liturgy* means
    a. a symbolic activity.
    b. random works.
    c. a ritual.
    d. participation in the work of God.

11. In liturgy the ___ continues today.
    a. early Church
    b. rosary
    c. Old Testament
    d. paschal mystery of Christ

12. Liturgical prayer is, above all, ___ prayer.
    a. private
    b. public
    c. musical
    d. silent

13. Christ's passion, death, resurrection, and ascension is
    a. the sacrifice of the Old Law.
    b. the Exodus.
    c. the paschal mystery.
    d. the Sabbath.

14. Liturgy has certain characteristics. Which one does *not* belong?
    a. It is complex in nature.
    b. It is addressed to God.
    c. It is the prayer of Christ.
    d. It is worship of the Trinity.

15. In the liturgy we always pray
    a. with the words of the Church.
    b. the stations of the cross.
    c. with Scripture only.
    d. to Mary.

Fill in the blank with the correct word(s).

16. The word *paschal* refers to the feast of _____.

17. The liturgical book containing the prayers for the Eucharist is called the

_____.

18. The public prayer of the Church is called _____.

19. At Mass the Scriptures are read from a book called the

_____.

20. A truth that continually calls us to deeper understanding is called a

_____.

For Extra Credit

If you sometimes find it difficult to concentrate at the liturgy, perhaps it is because you do not fully understand it. Tell some ways you could improve your liturgical experience.

Name _____ Date _____

Circle true or false.

1. The plan of God ended with the death of Jesus. **T** **F**

2. A sacrament actually brings about what it signifies. **T** **F**

3. Sacraments are something we just receive. **T** **F**

4. When a person baptizes, it is really Christ who baptizes. **T** **F**

5. The epiclesis is not essential to an understanding of a sacrament. **T** **F**

Circle the letter beside the best answer.

6. There are ___ sacraments.
   a. seven
   b. three
   c. five
   d. none of the above

7. God, first made visible in Jesus, is now made visible in
   a. the Church.
   b. priests.
   c. all clergy.
   d. all religious.

8. A sign is
   a. a mystery.
   b. something that points the way.
   c. the same as a sacrament.
   d. always invisible.

9. The Church calls the sacraments "God's
   a. signs."
   b. rituals."
   c. miracles."
   d. masterpieces."

10. Which of the following is *not* a purpose of the sacraments?
    a. to sanctify us
    b. to build up the Church
    c. to improve the lectionary
    d. to give praise and worship to God

11. Four essential qualities are present in each sacrament. Which of the following does *not* belong?
    a. music
    b. ritual action
    c. worship of God
    d. paschal mystery

12. A prayer that gives God glory is
    a. an epiclesis.
    b. a doxology.
    c. called anamnesis.
    d. a berakah.

13. The ___ contains Scripture readings to be proclaimed in the liturgy.
    a. sacramentary
    b. lectionary
    c. hymnal
    d. catechism

14. ___ is the liturgical act of remembering.
    a. Doxology
    b. Epiclesis
    c. Anamnesis
    d. Berakah

15. The berakah is
    a. an anamnesis.
    b. a specific prayer.
    c. a prayer form.
    d. a doxology only.

Fill in the blank with the correct word(s).

16. Catholics believe that Christ is truly _____ in the Eucharist.

17. The sacraments make the paschal mystery present through the power of the _____.

18. A _____ is a visible and effective sign through which we share God's grace.

19. The invisible life of God, first made visible in Jesus Christ, is now made visible in the _____.

20. In each sacrament we petition the Holy Spirit. The name for this is _____.

For Extra Credit

Describe the ways celebrating the sacraments strengthens your faith.

Circle true or false.

1. The Eucharist was not as important for the early Church as it is now. **T   F**

2. We are never more the Church than when we celebrate Eucharist. **T   F**

3. The central meaning of sacrifice is union with God. **T   F**

4. The Eucharist is both a sacrifice and a meal. **T   F**

5. The Eucharist is the celebration of the abiding presence of Jesus. **T   F**

Circle the letter beside the best answer.

6. When did Jesus institute the sacrament of Eucharist?
   a. the day he died
   b. the night before he died
   c. on Easter morning
   d. after his resurrection

7. The word *Eucharist* means
   a. remembering.
   b. blessing.
   c. reconciling.
   d. giving thanks.

8. *Epiclesis* means
   a. remembering.
   b. invocation.
   c. petitioning the Holy Spirit.
   d. calling upon the name of God.

9. The basic form of the eucharistic prayer is the
   a. berakah.
   b. invocation.
   c. epiclesis.
   d. grace.

10. Saint Paul told the Corinthians that they could not celebrate the Eucharist
    a. without recognizing the body of Christ, the Church.
    b. every Sunday.
    c. without one of the apostles present.
    d. often.

11. Which of the following gospels does *not* tell the story of the Last Supper?
    a. Matthew
    b. Mark
    c. Luke
    d. John

12. Which statement is *false*? The Eucharist is
    a. both a meal and a sacrifice.
    b. the sacrament of sacraments.
    c. the real presence of Christ.
    d. a symbol of Christ.

13. A ritual action that brings about and celebrates our union with God is called
    a. passover.
    b. mystery.
    c. sacrifice.
    d. meal.

14. In the Eucharist the paschal mystery of Christ
    a. is simply remembered.
    b. is just repeated.
    c. is truly made present.
    d. is absent.

15. When we receive Jesus in Communion we hear the words:
    a. "the sign of the cross."
    b. "Do this in memory of me."
    c. "Body of Christ."
    d. "I am with you always."

Fill in the blank with the correct word(s).

16. The Last Supper took place at the time of the Jewish

_____.

17. In the Holy Sacrifice of the Mass, the _____ is the external sign of the sacrifice.

18. The change of bread and wine into the Body and Blood of Christ is called

_____.

19. We become members of the body of Christ through Baptism, Eucharist, and _____.

20. The consecrated wine is truly the _____.

For Extra Credit

Paul learned in his conversion that what we do to one another we do to Christ. Do you believe that? How does it affect your life?

Circle true or false.

1. The external shape of the Mass is a meal. T F

2. When we gather together for the Eucharist we make the body of Christ visible. T F

3. The communion rite takes place during the preparation of the gifts. T F

4. Catholics consider the Eucharist primarily as a sacrament of healing. T F

5. The eucharistic prayer is part of the general intercessions. T F

Circle the letter beside the best answer.

6. Which of the following parts of the Eucharist includes the penitential rite?
  a. gathering
  b. storytelling
  c. meal sharing
  d. commissioning

7. The first two readings conclude with
  a. "The Lord be with you."
  b. "The word of the Lord."
  c. "Alleluia, alleluia."
  d. "The gospel of the Lord."

8. The profession of faith in the word we have heard proclaimed in the readings is called
  a. general intercessions.
  b. the gospel.
  c. the creed.
  d. the homily.

9. The Eucharist has a fourfold structure. Which item does *not* belong?
  a. storytelling
  b. personal testimonials
  c. meal sharing
  d. gathering

10. The central prayer of the Eucharist is the
  a. epiclesis.
  b. preface.
  c. eucharistic prayer.
  d. anamnesis.

Match Column A with Column B.

Column A

11. preface
12. homily
13. general intercessions
14. the Lord's Prayer
15. first reading

Column B

____ ordinarily taken from the Old Testament

____ connects the readings with our own lives

____ meal celebration

____ means "speaking in the presence of God"

____ prayers for the Church and for the world

____ part of the communion rite

____ statement of our faith

Briefly explain.

16. Liturgy of the Word: _____
_____
_____

17. general intercessions: _____
_____
_____

18. homily: _____
_____
_____

19. preparation of the gifts: _____
_____
_____

20. introductory rites: _____
_____
_____

For Extra Credit

Briefly describe how what you learned in this chapter can help you celebrate the Eucharist with more understanding and faith.

Circle true or false.

1. New members are initiated into the Church by receiving
   Baptism, Confirmation, and Eucharist.   T   F

2. Until they are baptized, catechumens may not participate fully
   in the Eucharist.   T   F

3. In certain cases anyone can baptize.   T   F

4. *To baptize* comes from a Greek word that means to begin again.   T   F

5. Turning to Christ takes place once and for all at Baptism.   T   F

Circle the letter beside the best answer.

6. ___ is coming to believe that Jesus Christ is
   the Savior of the world.
   a. Sacrifice
   b. Worship
   c. Ministry
   d. Conversion

7. The sacraments of initiation are
   a. Baptism, Confirmation, Reconciliation.
   b. Communion, Confirmation, Eucharist.
   c. Baptism, Confirmation, Eucharist.
   d. Confirmation, Reconciliation, Eucharist.

8. The root meaning of the word *catechumenate* is
   a. instruction.
   b. moral conversion.
   c. worship.
   d. ministry.

9. The catechumenate has four parts. Circle the
   one that does *not* belong.
   a. ministry
   b. moral conversion
   c. vigil
   d. instruction

10. Catechumens prepare for the sacraments of
    initiation especially
    a. at Christmas.
    b. at Easter.
    c. on Palm Sunday.
    d. during the season of Lent.

11. The white garment of the newly baptized
    symbolizes
    a. their first communion.
    b. that they have clothed themselves with
       Christ.
    c. that they have shed the garments of evil.
    d. their intention to serve others.

12. The Easter Vigil comes to its climax with the
    celebration of
    a. Baptism.
    b. Confirmation.
    c. Reconciliation.
    d. Eucharist.

13. Original sin is the absence of
    a. virtue.
    b. God's grace.
    c. weaknesses.
    d. repentance.

14. Baptism and Confirmation
    a. end our conversion.
    b. should be repeated if we sin excessively.
    c. give us an indelible spiritual mark.
    d. are received only by adults.

15. The sign of Confirmation is
    a. the pouring of water.
    b. anointing with oil.
    c. a white garment.
    d. bread and wine.

Fill in the blank with the correct word(s).

16. _____ is the process of coming to believe that Jesus Christ is the Savior.

17. The preparation for adults who wish to become Catholics is called the

_____.

18. A person who takes the first normal steps to becoming a Catholic is called

a _____.

19. In adult Baptism, the candidates are plunged into the water

_____ times.

20. _____ is a share in God's own life through the power of the Holy Spirit..

For Extra Credit.

Think of the images of Baptism you have learned. Which one do you find especially helpful? Explain.

Circle true or false.

1. The Eucharist is reserved in the tabernacle. T F

2. Churches are merely gathering places. T F

3. The most important purpose of a church is the celebration of the Eucharist. T F

4. In a church the altar is located in the narthex. T F

5. All churches include a separate eucharistic chapel. T F

Circle the letter beside the best answer.

6. Jesus said, "Destroy this temple and . . . I will raise it up." He was speaking about
   a. Jerusalem.
   b. the mountain.
   c. his own body.
   d. the Catholic Church.

7. ___ were originally built as public meeting places, not places of worship.
   a. Naves
   b. Basilicas
   c. Cathedrals
   d. Tabernacles

8. The congregation of a church gathers in the ___ to worship.
   a. apse
   b. ambry
   c. narthex
   d. nave

9. Another word for lectern is
   a. ambry.
   b. altar.
   c. ambo.
   d. apse.

10. The place where the sacrifice of Christ is made present under sacramental signs is
    a. the altar.
    b. the tabernacle.
    c. the baptistry.
    d. the ambo.

11. The word *tabernacle* comes from the Latin for
    a. tent.
    b. temple.
    c. gathering place.
    d. quiet place.

12. The word *Christ* means
    a. light.
    b. mission.
    c. anointed one.
    d. savior.

13. The place where Baptism takes place is the
    a. nave.
    b. sanctuary.
    c. baptistry.
    d. tabernacle.

14. The Eucharist reserved in the tabernacle is called
    a. Holy Communion.
    b. the Blessed Sacrament.
    c. the Eucharistic Prayer.
    d. the paschal mystery.

15. After the ___ the liturgy was celebrated in our own languages.
    a. Middle Ages
    b. Second Vatican Council
    c. earliest years of the Church
    d. Arian heresy

Match Column A with Column B.

Column A   **Column B**

16. apse   ____ niche in baptismal area for oils

17. nave   ____ lobby, porch, vestibule of a church

18. narthex   ____ semicircular domed area

19. tabernacle   ____ where the Eucharist is kept

20. ambry   ____ building for baptism

                              ____ large open assembly area

For Extra Credit

In what way are you "a living stone"?

Respond.

21. Describe what happens at the Commissioning Rite at Mass. _____

_____

_____

_____

_____

_____

22. What do we remember on Holy Thursday? Good Friday? Easter Sunday?
What should we remember about all three mysteries together?

_____

_____

_____

_____

_____

23. Explain briefly what happens during the Liturgy of the Word.

_____

_____

_____

_____

_____

24. Explain why Baptism is both a being born and a dying. _____

_____

_____

_____

_____

25. What are the principal effects of Baptism?_____

_____

_____

_____

_____

For Extra Credit

What do you think is God's plan for you? How do you think you can begin to fulfill it right now? In what ways can the Church help you?

Circle true or false.

1. Sunday is the day on which Christ died. **T   F**

2. The seasons of the liturgical year give variety to the liturgy. **T   F**

3. In the United States, Catholics over fourteen are bound to fast on Good Friday. **T   F**

4. The Christian celebration of Sunday is like the Jewish sabbath. **T   F**

5. One of the main purposes of Christian fasting is to lose weight. **T   F**

Circle the letter beside the best answer.

6. The different seasons of the liturgical year
   a. exist for the sake of variety.
   b. help us see the paschal mystery from different angles.
   c. all show us the same view of the paschal mystery.
   d. mostly help us remember the past.

7. At the time of Jesus, Sunday was called
   a. the seventh day of the week.
   b. the Sabbath.
   c. Passover.
   d. the first day of the week.

8. Lent begins on Ash Wednesday and extends to
   a. Easter Sunday.
   b. Palm Sunday.
   c. Good Friday.
   d. Holy Thursday.

9. The Church's image of Lent is, above all, that of
   a. new life.
   b. ashes.
   c. fasting.
   d. penance.

10. Baptism gives us the spiritual mark we call
    a. rebirth.
    b. repentance.
    c. character.
    d. purity.

11. Baptism is both a dying and a
    a. burying.
    b. sacrificial.
    c. rising.
    d. repentance.

12. Which of the following is *not* a purpose of fasting and abstinence?
    a. reflection
    b. sorrow for sin
    c. a more serious approach to Christian life
    d. maintaining an unchanged life

13. ___ was originally called the Christian Passover.
    a. Sunday
    b. Saturday
    c. Easter
    d. Christmas

14. ___ is the most prevalent scriptural theme found throughout the Triduum.
    a. The Lamb of God
    b. Fire
    c. Darkness and light
    d. The meal

15. The oldest Christian feast is
    a. Christmas.
    b. Easter.
    c. Sunday.
    d. Passover.

Fill in the blank with the correct word(s).

16. The two main seasons of the Church year are Christmas-Advent and

_____.

17. The seasons between the two main liturgical seasons are called

_____.

18. The *original* Christian feast day is not Christmas or Easter but

_____.

19. For the Jews the sabbath is primarily a day of _____.

20. The resurrection tells us that death will be overcome by new

_____.

For Extra Credit

Do you believe that the resurrection is happening *now*? Explain your answer.

Circle true or false.

1. The Great Fifty Days comes after Easter Sunday.   T   F

2. *Mystagogy* is a time for reflecting on the truths of our faith.   T   F

3. The gift of the Holy Spirit is given to us freely before any good work of ours.   T   F

4. Advent extends from the First Sunday of Advent until December 24.   T   F

5. Ordinary Time in the liturgical year means "usual" or "average."   T   F

Circle the letter beside the best answer.

6. A newly initiated Christian is called a
   a. catechumen.
   b. mystagogue.
   c. neophyte.
   d. pentecostal.

7. ___/Acts is meant to be read as a unit.
   a. Matthew
   b. Mark
   c. Luke
   d. John

8. On the final day of our fifty-day celebration of Easter we celebrate
   a. Easter Sunday.
   b. Pentecost.
   c. Holy Thursday.
   d. Good Friday.

9. The seven gifts of the Holy Spirit are also called
   a. ruahs.
   b. fruits.
   c. chrisms.
   d. charisms.

10. The gift of the Holy Spirit to the Church is primarily a gift of
    a. mission.
    b. celebration.
    c. preparation.
    d. meditation.

Match Column A with Column B.

Column A

11. Lent

12. Easter

13. Great Fifty Days

14. Advent

15. Ordinary Time

Column B

_____ joyful expectation of Christ's coming

_____ "the Feast of feasts"

_____ reflection on the entire life and work of Jesus Christ

_____ preparation for Baptism

_____ incarnation

_____ the Easter season

Fill in the blank with the correct word(s).

16. God radically changed the universe through the _____ _____ of Jesus Christ.

17. _____ comes from the Greek word meaning "fifty."

18. The candles in the Advent wreath symbolize the light of _____.

19. When Jesus appeared to the disciples on the evening of his resurrection he gave them the power to _____.

20. The word spirit comes from a Hebrew word _ruah_ meaning _____.

For Extra Credit

We are usually most aware of the "big" feasts of the Church, but what is special about Ordinary Time? How can it help you grow closer to Christ?

Circle true or false.

1. The sacrament of Reconciliation is just for confessing serious sins. **T   F**

2. Jesus gave his apostles the power to forgive sins. **T   F**

3. In the early Church canonical penance was celebrated only once in a person's lifetime. **T   F**

4. Like the Eucharist, Reconciliation celebrates the paschal mystery of Christ. **T   F**

5. Sin simply means breaking the rules. **T   F**

Circle the letter beside the best answer.

6. The story of the prodigal son demonstrates
   a. God's disappointment in us.
   b. God's anger with our sins.
   c. God's love and forgiveness.
   d. God's satisfaction with us.

7. Which of the following was *not* a way sins were forgiven in the early Church?
   a. prayer
   b. almsgiving
   c. fasting
   d. exile

8. Circle the answer that does *not* belong. The principal effects of the sacrament of Reconciliation include
   a. forgiveness.
   b. pardon.
   c. physical healing.
   d. peace.

9. The expression of sorrow for our sins is called the
   a. Act of Contrition.
   b. Lord's Prayer.
   c. Creed.
   d. absolution.

10. The sacrament of Reconciliation is meant to
    a. make us feel guilty.
    b. encourage us to blame ourselves.
    c. heal what is broken in us by sin.
    d. make us be overly concerned with sin.

11. We are *obliged* to confess
    a. venial sins only.
    b. mortal sins only.
    c. all sins mortal and venial.
    d. original sin.

12. The proclamation of God's forgiveness in Reconciliation is called
    a. thanksgiving.
    b. confession.
    c. absolution.
    d. contrition.

13. Which of the following is *not* part of the individual rite of Reconciliation?
    a. preparation of gifts
    b. contrition
    c. confession
    d. satisfaction

14. Reconciliation gives us the opportunity to be healed from the weakness of our
    a. venial sins.
    b. neighbors.
    c. physical sufferings.
    d. Baptism.

15. ___ means repairing the harm our sins have done.
    a. Contrition
    b. Satisfaction
    c. Reconciliation
    d. Confession

23

Fill in the blank with the correct word(s).

16. In the sacrament of _____ our relationship to God and to the Church is restored.

17. Sorrow for having sinned is called _____.

18. The obligation the priest has never to reveal what he has heard in Reconciliation is called the _____.

19. If you are physically able, you must confess mortal sins before you can receive _____.

20. We give satisfaction for our sins by doing a _____.

For Extra Credit

How do you feel about Reconciliation? Are you ever embarrassed or unwilling to participate in this sacrament? If so, did this chapter help you overcome any of your fears?

Circle true or false.

1. Suffering and illness exist because God wants them to exist. **T   F**

2. The sacrament of the Anointing of the Sick must always take place in a church. **T   F**

3. Anointing of the Sick is a sacrament of initiation. **T   F**

4. To receive the sacrament of the Anointing of the Sick one must be in danger of death. **T   F**

5. The focus of the sacrament of Anointing is on healing. **T   F**

Circle the letter beside the best answer.

6. Illness
   a. is what God wants for us.
   b. can help to deepen our faith.
   c. is merely punishment for our sins.
   d. is impossible if we have faith.

7. The Letter of James emphasizes the importance of ___ in every aspect of our lives.
   a. prayer
   b. relationships
   c. health
   d. illness

8. The essential rite of the sacrament of the Anointing of the Sick is the
   a. imposition of hands.
   b. invocation.
   c. anointing with oil.
   d. forgiveness of sins.

9. Anointing of the Sick was formerly called
   a. Laying on of hands.
   b. Viaticum.
   c. Conversion.
   d. Extreme Unction.

10. Who probably would *not* be eligible to receive the sacrament of Anointing?
    a. alcoholics
    b. the mentally ill
    c. someone going into surgery
    d. someone with a cold

Match Column A with Column B.

Column A

11. laying on of hands

12. anointing with oil

13. Viaticum

14. Anointing of the Sick

15. Extreme Unction

Column B

____ Holy Communion given to the dying

____ Holy Communion given to children

____ the essential rite of the sacrament of Anointing

____ former name for the sacrament of Anointing

____ physical miracles

____ liturgical sacrament of healing

____ interaction between the community and the sick

____ ancient sign of blessing

Fill in the blank with the correct word(s).

16. The _____ used in Anointing of the Sick is blessed by the bishop on Holy Thursday.

17. Anointing of the Sick is mainly a sacrament of _____.

18. Holy Communion given to the dying is called _____.

19. The priest anoints the sick person's _____ and _____ during the celebration of Anointing.

20. One of the key symbolic actions of the sacrament takes place when the priest _____ on the sick person.

For Extra Credit

How can our faith give us a new way to look at illness and suffering?

Circle true or false.

1. The Church confers the sacrament of Holy Orders only on baptized men. **T   F**

2. The authority of bishops and priests comes from within them. **T   F**

3. The sacrament of Holy Orders is given only once. **T   F**

4. Only bishops share in the authority of Jesus Christ. **T   F**

5. A permanent deacon cannot be married. **T   F**

Circle the letter beside the best answer.

6. In the sacrament of Holy Orders the presbyterate is the order of
   a. bishops.
   b. priests.
   c. sisters.
   d. deacons.

7. Which of the following events best symbolizes the apostles' call to service?
   a. the Last Supper
   b. Jesus' choosing the Twelve
   c. Jesus' washing the apostles' feet
   d. the resurrection

8. Holy Orders is the sacrament through which the ___ given by Christ to the apostles continues in the Church.
   a. mission
   b. anointing
   c. prayers
   d. Blessed Trinity

9. The successors of the apostles are called
   a. bishops.
   b. priests.
   c. deacons.
   d. disciples.

10. A bishop can be ordained only by
    a. a priest.
    b. a deacon.
    c. a cardinal.
    d. another bishop.

11. The essential rite of ordination includes
    a. the laying on of hands and the prayer of consecration.
    b. the anointing and the giving of the chasuble.
    c. the giving of the stole and absolution.
    d. the gifts of bread and wine.

12. A new priest is invested with the ___ as a symbol of the priesthood.
    a. crosier
    b. dalmatic
    c. chasuble
    d. miter

13. The word ___ comes from a Greek word meaning "to serve."
    a. bishop
    b. presbyter
    c. deacon
    d. dalmatic

14. ___ was the first deacon.
    a. Jesus
    b. Stephen
    c. Paul
    d. Peter

15. A deacon
    a. is a successor to the apostles.
    b. is the auxiliary of the bishop.
    c. assists the bishops and priests.
    d. leads his local church.

Match Column A with Column B.

Column A

16. ring

17. miter

18. crosier

19. Book of the Gospels

20. prostration

Column B

_____ rite of authority

_____ symbol of bishop's role as teacher and preacher of the word of God

_____ symbol of fidelity to the Church

_____ symbol of humble and sincere prayer

_____ signifies the role of the bishop as a herald of truth

_____ essential sign of ordination

_____ symbol of bishop's role of pastor

For Extra Credit

Besides prayer, what do you think are some ways that can help you discover your vocation?

Circle true or false.

1. The sacrament of Matrimony reflects the relationship Christ has with the Church. **T F**

2. In the sacrament of Matrimony, both the man and the woman must be baptized. **T F**

3. Marriage is a sacred covenant. **T F**

4. A commitment to love is based on feelings alone. **T F**

5. The Church forbids natural methods of birth control. **T F**

Circle the letter beside the best answer.

6. The sacrament of Matrimony
   a. is mostly a legal agreement.
   b. is basically a romance and a wedding.
   c. creates a sacred covenant.
   d. is a completely private act.

7. Hosea compared ___ to a faithful husband and Israel to a loving bride.
   a. Peter
   b. Jesus
   c. David
   d. God

8. The word *banns* means
   a. valid.
   b. proclamations.
   c. invitations.
   d. commitment.

9. Marriage preparation
   a. takes place in Pre-Cana classes.
   b. is optional.
   c. is only necessary if one of the people is not Catholic.
   d. is necessary for the witnesses as well as the engaged couple.

10. Catholics must marry in the presence of a priest or deacon and
    a. their parents.
    b. acolytes.
    c. a judge.
    d. two witnesses.

11. Which of the following is *not* an essential sign of the sacrament of Matrimony?
    a. the presence of a priest
    b. the presence of two witnesses
    c. the free consent of the couple
    d. the exchange of rings

12. When we marry we promise fidelity to one person and
    a. lifelong happiness.
    b. the giving up of self.
    c. a permanent commitment.
    d. frequent communion.

13. The sacrament of Matrimony is a life-giving sign of God's
    a. grace for the lifetime of the couple.
    b. presence at the wedding ceremony.
    c. healing power.
    d. none of the above

29

14. In the Christian ideal of marriage
    a. a man and a woman are partners.
    b. a couple chooses whether they will have children.
    c. the couple should not use *any* form of birth control.
    d. at least one person should be baptized.

15. Circle the answer that does *not* belong. A married couple reflects God's love in
    a. their romantic attachment to each other.
    b. their unity of body, heart, and soul.
    c. the indissolubility of their vows.
    d. their openness to having children.

Fill in the blank with the correct word(s).

16. The Church calls the family "the domestic _____."

17. For a Catholic marriage to be valid, you must marry in the presence of _____ and two witnesses.

18. _____ are the ministers of the sacrament of Matrimony.

19. Catholics believe that the sacrament of Matrimony is an _____ bond, one that can never be broken.

20. For Catholics a marriage is not valid without _____ consent.

For Extra Credit

What are some things you think could be difficult in a marriage? Why is maturity important?

Circle true or false.

1. The word *saint* refers only to historical men and women of exceptional holiness. **T F**

2. Our great hope from the communion of saints is that saints will work miracles for us. **T F**

3. We adore and worship the saints. **T F**

4. God's holiness is a shared gift. **T F**

5. All Christians who have lived holy lives are saints. **T F**

Circle the letter beside the best answer.

6. Which of the following statements is *false*?
   a. The saints help us by their prayers.
   b. We honor saints because of their holiness.
   c. Salvation and holiness are communal.
   d. Ordinary people are not expected to be saints.

7. Who of the following are honored by a *solemnity*?
   a. Mary
   b. Stephen
   c. the archangels
   d. the Holy Innocents

8. Who of the following are honored on a *feast*?
   a. Saints Peter and Paul
   b. the apostles
   c. John the Baptist
   d. Joseph

9. On *memorial* days the Church celebrates
   a. the birthday of a saint.
   b. a saint's day of death.
   c. holy people who are still alive.
   d. the memory of our Church Fathers.

10. Which of the following is *not* an American saint?
    a. Saint Charles Lwanga
    b. Blessed Kateri Tekakwitha
    c. Saint Frances Xavier Cabrini
    d. Saint Elizabeth Ann Seton

11. Which of the following is *not* one of the four principal privileges of Mary? She is
    a. Mother of God.
    b. Blessed Virgin.
    c. the Immaculate Conception.
    d. the Ascension.

12. ___ means that Mary was redeemed and free from all sin from the beginning of her life.
    a. The ascension
    b. The assumption
    c. The immaculate conception
    d. Virgin

13. Genuine devotion to Mary emphasizes, above all, that she is
    a. Mother of God and model disciple.
    b. worker of miracles.
    c. equal to her Son, Jesus.
    d. the one who gave us the rosary.

14. ___ is at the heart of the rosary.
    a. Meditation on the mysteries
    b. The Hail Mary
    c. The annunciation
    d. Devotion

15. What feast of Mary is celebrated on August 15?
    a. the annunciation
    b. the assumption
    c. the visitation
    d. the immaculate conception

31

Fill in the blank with the correct word(s).

16. Our union with God and the saints is called the _____

_____.

17. The word *saint* means _____.

18. The most important days on the Church calendar are called

_____.

19. The Church recognizes the extraordinary holiness of a person through the process of _____.

20. _____ miracles are required before formal declaration of sainthood.

For Extra Credit

Do you feel like a saint? How can you grow in holiness?

Circle the letter beside the best answer.

1. Circle the one that does *not* belong.
   A liturgical ritual is
   a. private.
   b. interpersonal.
   c. repetitive.
   d. acted out.

2. Scripture is part of
   a. two sacramental celebrations only.
   b. every liturgical celebration.
   c. every sacrament except Matrimony.
   d. the liturgy if it fits with the theme.

3. The liturgical term for *petition* is
   a. doxology.
   b. anamnesis.
   c. berakah.
   d. epiclesis.

4. The Mass is, above all,
   a. a memorial meal.
   b. a sign of bread and wine.
   c. both a meal and a sacrifice.
   d. just an image of Good Friday.

5. The Church teaches that when we receive
   the Eucharist worthily
   a. mortal sins are forgiven.
   b. our venial sins are forgiven.
   c. we are preserved from temptation forever.
   d. we need do nothing more to be holy.

6. Mystagogy is primarily a time for
   a. repentance.
   b. reflecting on the mysteries of faith.
   c. fasting and abstinence.
   d. conversion.

7. The catechumenate has four parts. Circle the
   one that does *not* belong.
   a. a vigil
   b. instruction
   c. ministry
   d. worship

8. The Christian celebration of Sunday is
   primarily
   a. like the Jewish sabbath.
   b. a time to celebrate the sacraments of
   initiation.
   c. a day to assemble for worship.
   d. a day off.

9. Choose the one that does *not* belong. The
   seasons of the liturgical year are
   a. Advent-Christmas.
   b. Ordinary Time.
   c. Pentecost.
   d. Lent-Easter.

10. The sacrament of Reconciliation
    a. is a sacrament of healing.
    b. is a celebration of love and forgiveness.
    c. celebrates our continuing conversion.
    d. all of the above

11. The essential sign of Anointing of the Sick is
    a. absolution.
    b. anointing with oil.
    c. prayer of the faithful.
    d. witnesses.

12. Circle the one that does *not* belong. The
    ranks of Holy Orders include
    a. the deaconate.
    b. the vowed religious.
    c. the presbyterate.
    d. the episcopate.

Define.

13. liturgy: _____

_____

_____

14. sacrament: _____

_____

_____

15. conversion: _____

_____

_____

16. paschal mystery: _____

_____

_____

17. Eucharist: _____

_____

_____

18. Reconciliation: _____

_____

_____

19. sacrifice: _____

_____

_____

20. absolution: _____

_____

_____

21. Matrimony: _____

_____

_____

22. communion: _____

_____

_____

23. Triduum: _____

_____

_____

Respond.

24. Describe real love and what it means in a Christian marriage.

_____

_____

_____

_____

_____

_____

_____

_____

25. What meaning does the resurrection have in the life of a Christian?

_____

_____

_____

_____

_____

_____

_____

For Extra Credit

Did you learn something in this course that completely surprised you or that changed your view on prayer or the sacraments? Explain.

Read each statement. Circle the response that indicates your beliefs about Liturgy and Worship.

A: I believe strongly   **B:** I have questions about it   **C:** I do not know

1. I am called to worship God.   A B C

2. The Son of God, the second Person of the Blessed Trinity, became one of us in Jesus.   A B C

3. In the sacraments I am saved, forgiven, and made one with Jesus Christ.   A B C

4. The Eucharist is the center of my life of faith.   A B C

5. The Eucharist is truly the Body and Blood of Jesus Christ.   A B C

6. Faith in Christ—coming to believe that Jesus is the Savior of the world—is a lifelong task.   A B C

7. I am always in need of God's grace.   A B C

8. Because of the resurrection, evil will never win in the end. God's love and life will triumph.   A B C

9. The sacraments are essential to my life as a Catholic.   A B C

10. I am called to bring Christ to the world by word and example.   A B C

Read each statement. Circle the response that best expresses the way you are living your faith.

A: Yes!   **B:** Usually   **C:** Sometimes   **D:** No

1. I celebrate the Eucharist every week.   A B C D

2. My faith in Christ affects my daily life.   A B C D

3. Prayer is a part of my daily life.   A B C D

4. I see the sacraments as real encounters with Jesus Christ.   A B C D

5. I am a Catholic who practices what I believe.   A B C D

6. I see the importance of worshiping together with other Catholics.   A B C D

7. I know that I am chosen and loved by God.   A B C D

8. Symbols and rituals of my faith help me to pray and worship.   A B C D

9. I make an effort to be part of the liturgical life of the Church.   A B C D

10. I am a faithful disciple of Jesus Christ.   A B C D

Five important ideas that have helped me in this course:

1. _____
   _____

2. _____
   _____

3. _____
   _____

4. _____
   _____

5. _____
   _____

Some questions I have are:

Test 1

True/False
1. T   2. F   3. T   4. F   5. T

Circling
6. c   7. d   8. c   9. b   10. b
11. d   12. c   13. c   14. d
15. b

Fill in the blank
16. Catholic Church
17. mountains/hills   18. rituals
19. prodigal/lost   20. symbol

For Extra Credit
Accept reasonable answers.

Test 2

True/False
1. T   2. T   3. F   4. T   5. T

Circling
6. d   7. a   8. b   9. a   10. d
11. d   12. b   13. c   14. a
15. a

Fill in the blank
16. Passover   17. sacramentary
18. liturgy   19. lectionary
20. mystery

For Extra Credit
Accept reasonable answers.

Test 3

True/False
1. F   2. T   3. F   4. T   5. F

Circling
6. a   7. a   8. b   9. d   10. c
11. a   12. b   13. b   14. c
15. c

Fill in the blank
16. present   17. Holy Spirit
18. sacrament   19. Church
20. epiclesis

For Extra Credit
Accept reasonable answers.

Test 4

True/False
1. F   2. T   3. T   4. T   5. T

Circling
6. b   7. d   8. c   9. a   10. a
11. d   12. d   13. c   14. c
15. c

Fill in the blank
16. Passover   17. meal
18. transubstantiation
19. Confirmation   20. Precious
Blood/Blood of Christ

For Extra Credit
Accept reasonable answers.

Test 5

True/False
1. T   2. T   3. F   4. F   5. F

Circling
6. a   7. b   8. c   9. b   10. c

Matching
15, 12, ___, 11, 13, 14, ___

Define
16. See page 58.   17. See page
59.   18. See page 58.   19. See
page 60.   20. See page 57.

For Extra Credit
Accept reasonable answers.

Test 6

True/False
1. T   2. T   3. T   4. F   5. F

Circling
6. d   7. c   8. a   9. c   10. d
11. b   12. d   13. b   14. c
15. b

Fill in the blank
16. conversion   17. Rite of
Christian Initiation of Adults/
RCIA   18. catechumen
19. three   20. sanctifying grace

For Extra Credit
Accept reasonable answers.

Test 7

True/False
1. T   2. F   3. T   4. F   5. F

Circling
6. c   7. b   8. d   9. c   10. a
11. a   12. c   13. c   14. b
15. b

Matching
20, 18, 16, 19, ___, 17

For Extra Credit
Accept reasonable answers.

Midsemester Test

True/False
1. F   2. F   3. F   4. T   5. T

Circling
6. c   7. d   8. b   9. c   10. b

Explain
11. See page 68.   12. See pages
68–69.   13. See page 75.
14. See page 83.   15. See page
84.   16. See pages 22–23.
17. See page 35.   18. See page
38.   19. See page 38.   20. See
pages 48–49.   21. See pages
62–63.   22. See pages 46–49.
23. See page 58.   24. See page
72.   25. See pages 72, 75.

For Extra Credit
Accept reasonable responses.

Test 8

True/False
1. F   2. T   3. F   4. F   5. F

Circling
6. b   7. d   8. d   9. a   10. c
11. c   12. d   13. c   14. a
15. c

Fill in the blank
16. Easter-Lent   17. Ordinary
Time   18. Sunday   19. rest
20. life

For Extra Credit
Accept reasonable answers.

Answer Key

Test 9

True/False

1. T   2. T   3. T   4. T   5. F

Circling

6. c   7. c   8. b   9. d   10. a

Matching

14, 12, 15, 11, ___, 13

Fill in the blank

16. paschal mystery

17. Pentecost   18. faith/Christ

19. forgive/reconcile

20. wind/breath/air

For Extra Credit

Accept reasonable answers.

Test 10

True/False

1. F   2. T   3. T   4. T   5. F

Circling

6. c   7. d   8. c   9. a   10. c

11. b   12. c   13. a   14. a

15. b

Fill in the blank

16. Reconciliation

17. contrition   18. seal of

confession   19. Holy

Communion/Eucharist

20. penance

For Extra Credit

Accept reasonable answers.

Test 11

True/False

1. F   2. F   3. F   4. F   5. T

Circling

6. b   7. a   8. c   9. d   10. d

Matching

13, ___, 12, 15, ___, 14, ___, 11

Fill in the blank

16. olive oil   17. healing

18. Viaticum   19. forehead,

palms   20. lays hands

For Extra Credit

Accept reasonable answers.

Test 12

True/False

1. T   2. F   3. T   4. F   5. F

Circling

6. b   7. c   8. a   9. a   10. d

11. a   12. c   13. c   14. b

15. c

Matching

___, 19, 16, 20, 17, ___, 18

For Extra Credit

Accept reasonable answers.

Test 13

True/False

1. T   2. T   3. T   4. F   5. F

Circling

6. c   7. d   8. b   9. a   10. d

11. d   12. c   13. a   14. a

15. a

Fill in the blank

16. Church   17. a priest

18. the bride and groom

19. indissoluble   20. free

For Extra Credit

Accept reasonable answers.

Test 14

True/False

1. F   2. F   3. F   4. T   5. T

Circling

6. d   7. a   8. b   9. b   10. a

11. d   12. c   13. a   14. a

15. b

Fill in the blank

16. communion of saints

17. holy   18. solemnities

19. canonization   20. three

For Extra Credit

Accept reasonable answers.

Final Test

Circling

1. a   2. b   3. d   4. c   5. b

6. b   7. a   8. c   9. c   10. d

11. b   12. b

Define

13. See page 22.   14. See page

35.   15. See page 69.   16. See

page 24.   17. See page 45.

18. See page 117.   19. See

page 47.   20. See page 119.

21. See page 153.   22. See

page 62.   23. See page 98.

Respond

24. See pages 153–154.

25. See page 95.

For Extra Credit

Accept reasonable answers.